*Grandma's Full Name*

_____   _____
Date of Birth   Place of Birth

_____
Grandma's Mother's Full Name

_____   _____
Date of Birth   Place of Birth

_____
Grandma's Father's Full Name

_____   _____
Date of Birth   Place of Birth

Grandma

Her stories. Her words.

COMPENDIUM™
INCORPORATED

live inspired.

WITH SPECIAL THANKS TO

Jason Aldrich, Gerry Baird, Jay Baird, Neil Beaton, Josie Bissett, Laura Boro, Melissa Carlson, Tiffany Parente Connors, Jim & Alyssa Darragh & Family, Rob Estes, Pamela Farrington, Michael & Leianne Flynn & Family, Sarah Forster, Michael J. Hedge, Liz Heinlein & Family, Renee & Brad Holmes, Jennifer Hurwitz, Heidi Jones, Sheila Kamuda, Michelle Kim, Carol Anne Kennedy, June Martin, David Miller, Carin Moore, Jessica Phoenix and Tom DesLongchamp, Janet Potter & Family, Joanna Price, Heidi & Jose Rodriguez, Diane Roger, Alie Satterlee, Sam T. Schick, Kirsten & Garrett Sessions, Andrea Summers, Brien Thompson, Helen Tsao, Anne Whiting, Kobi & Heidi Yamada & Family, Justi and Tote Yamada & Family, Bob and Val Yamada, Kaz & Kristin Yamada & Family, Tai & Joy Yamada, Anne Zadra, August & Arline Zadra, Gus & Rosie Zadra.

CREDITS

Compiled by Dan Zadra

Designed by Steve Potter

Created by Kobi Yamada

ISBN: 978-1-935414-04-9

Printed in China

Dear Grandma,

This little book is one of the most meaningful gifts we could ever share together. It won't take long for you to respond to the questions in these pages, but future generations of our family will treasure your answers forever.

Imagine if your mother or grandmother had been able to tuck away a similar book for you. What a thrill to discover a few of their favorite memories from the old days, in their own handwriting. Well, now is your chance to create a wonderful family heirloom of your own.

Like a trip down memory lane, the following pages will whisk you back to another time and place. The questions are simple, but only you can provide the answers—and that's what makes this book so special.

Grandma, can you describe the house you grew up in? What was your old neighborhood like? What's the best thing about having grandchildren? Have fun with your answers—they don't need to be complicated or formal. Just answer straight from the heart and the result is sure to be magical to those who love you.

Grandma, what do you know about the origins of your maiden name? What nationality or culture is it associated with?

_____

_____

_____

_____

_____

_____

_____

_____

Grandma, how, when, and why did your ancestors first come to this country?

_____

_____

_____

_____

_____

_____

_____

Grandma, what do you remember about your own grandmother and grandfather? How and where did they meet and decide to get married?

_____

_____

_____

_____

_____

_____

_____

_____

Grandma, what was your mom like? Can you tell a story that describes her personality or values?

_____

_____

_____

_____

_____

_____

_____

_____

_____

Grandma, what was your dad like? Can you tell a story that describes his personality or values?

_____

_____

_____

_____

_____

_____

_____

_____

_____

Grandma, are there any heroes, famous people, colorful characters, or notorious "black sheep" in your family?

_____

_____

_____

_____

_____

_____

_____

_____

_____

Grandma, can you describe the house you grew up in? What was your bedroom like? How about the kitchen, living room and backyard?

_____

_____

_____

_____

_____

_____

_____

_____

_____

Grandma, when you were little, what was bedtime like in your family?
Did your parents ever read stories or sing to you?

_____

_____

_____

_____

_____

_____

_____

_____

_____

Grandma, when you were a child, what did you want to be when you grew up?

_____

_____

_____

_____

_____

_____

_____

Grandma, thinking back to when you were a child, can you describe the places you went to play in the neighborhood? The woods? A treehouse? A pool or park?

_____

_____

_____

_____

_____

_____

_____

_____

Grandma, do you remember any stories that your parents or grandparents used to tell about hard times or the good old days?

_____

_____

_____

_____

_____

_____

_____

_____

_____

Grandma, how far away were your grade school and high school—
and how did you get there each day?

_____

_____

_____

_____

_____

_____

_____

_____

Grandma, when you were in school, which were your favorite and least favorite classes, and which extracurricular activities did you participate in?

_____

_____

_____

_____

_____

_____

_____

_____

_____

Grandma, what were the costs of everyday things such as food, clothes, movies, etc., when you were a kid?

_____

_____

_____

_____

_____

_____

_____

_____

_____

Grandma, what were typical family meals in your house when you were growing up—and what were school lunches like for you?

_____

_____

_____

_____

_____

_____

_____

_____

Grandma, when you were a child, what were the rules at your house, including the rules for dating and curfew?

_____

_____

_____

_____

_____

_____

_____

_____

Grandma, in your life so far, what talents or abilities seem to come to you most easily? Is there anything that you are a "natural" at?

_____

_____

_____

_____

_____

_____

_____

_____

Grandma, can you remember a particular tragedy, illness, setback or difficult time in your life—and how you got through it?

_____

_____

_____

_____

_____

_____

_____

_____

_____

Grandma, when you were growing up, what was your favorite holiday or special occasion, and how did your family celebrate it?

Grandma, what are your best childhood memories from summer
vacation or camp?

_____

_____

_____

_____

_____

_____

_____

_____

Grandma, when you were a teenager, what were some of your favorite movies, songs, dances, musical groups, or entertainers?

_____

_____

_____

_____

_____

_____

_____

_____

Grandma, how did you and Grandpa meet, and what kind of dates did you go on together?

_____

_____

_____

_____

_____

_____

_____

_____

Grandma, can you describe what it was like raising a family, including some of the sacrifices you had to make?

_____

_____

_____

_____

_____

_____

_____

_____

Grandma, have you ever experienced a natural disaster such as an earthquake, hurricane, forest fire, tornado, snowstorm or flood— and what was it like?

_____

_____

_____

_____

_____

_____

_____

_____

Grandma, what's an important lesson your parents taught you—
something you've tried to live by and share with your own kids?

_____

_____

_____

_____

_____

_____

_____

_____

_____

Grandma, what are the things you value most in your life?

_____

_____

_____

_____

_____

_____

_____

_____

_____

_____

Grandma, can you describe two or three major news or political events in your lifetime and how they impacted your life or the lives of those around you?

_____

_____

_____

_____

_____

_____

_____

_____

Grandma, what are some of the things you miss most about the "old days" with your friends or family?

_____

_____

_____

_____

_____

_____

_____

_____

Grandma, what are your highest hopes for your grandchildren?

_____

_____

_____

_____

_____

_____

_____

_____

_____

Grandma, describe some old family keepsakes, photos or heirlooms that have special sentimental value to you—and why?

_____

_____

_____

_____

_____

_____

_____

Grandma, what have been some of your proudest or happiest moments in life so far?

_____

_____

_____

_____

_____

_____

_____

_____

Grandma, are there any family recipes that were handed down to you? Which of your own recipes deserve to be handed down to your children and grandchildren?

_____

_____

_____

_____

_____

_____

_____

_____

Grandma, in what ways do your children make you proud?

_____

_____

_____

_____

_____

_____

_____

_____

_____

_____

Grandma, what are some of the best things about having grandchildren?

_____

_____

_____

_____

_____

_____

_____

_____

_____

Grandma, in what ways has the world changed for the better
(and the worse) since you were a kid?

_____

_____

_____

_____

_____

_____

_____

_____

Grandma, looking back, what are some of the things you are most grateful for?

_____

_____

_____

_____

_____

_____

_____

_____

Grandma, what are your secrets for staying young at heart?

_____

_____

_____

_____

_____

_____

_____

_____

Grandma, at the end of your life, how would you like your children and grandchildren to remember you?

Memories are perhaps the best gifts of all.

—Gloria Gaither